Follow My Leader!

Emma Chichester Clark

A

Andersen Press
London

for Finn

143344

Along the path,
Hopping and skipping,
Follow my leader!

Through the trees,
Whirling and twirling,
Follow my leader!

Over the stile,
Leaping and bounding,
Follow my leader!

Up the hill,
Puffing and panting,
Follow my leader!

Round the corner,
Jumping and jiving,
Follow my leader!

Down the steps,
Bumping and thumping,
Follow my leader!

Across the stream,
Splishing and splashing,
Follow my leader!

Into the woods,
Shouting and roaring,
Follow my leader!

But wait . . .
Can you hear it?
Shhh! What's that noise?

"I want to play,"
The tiger said, smiling.

"Well," said the boy,
"Just let me see . . ."

"All right," he said slowly,
"You are the leader,
But the rules of the game are . . .
You MUSTN'T turn round!"

The tiger roared,
"READY?"

Out of the woods,
Shouting and roaring,
Follow my leader!

Across the stream,
Splishing and splashing,
Follow my leader!

Up the steps,
Bumping and thumping,
Follow my leader!

Round the corner,
Jumping and jiving,
Follow my leader!

Down the hill,
Puffing and panting,
Follow my leader!

Over the stile,
Leaping and bounding,
Follow my leader!

Through the trees,
Whirling and twirling,
Follow my leader!

Up the path,
Skipping and hopping,
Follow my leader!

Through the gate,
Quickly and quietly,
Follow my leader!

Close the door,
Grinning and gasping,
Follow my leader!

See him go,
Dancing and prancing,
Follow my leader,
Follow my leader,
Follow my leader,
RRROOOAAr!